KINDNE

by

Carole MacKenthun, R.S.M.
and Paulinus Dwyer, O.P.

illustrated by Vanessa Filkins

Cover by Vanessa Filkins

Songs by Kathy Jones, Frances Mann Benson
and Helen Kitchell Evans

Shining Star Publications, Copyright © 1987
A Division of Good Apple, Inc.

ISBN No. 0-86653-379-6

Standardized Subject Code TA ac

Printing No. 987654

Shining Star Publications
A Division of Good Apple, Inc.
Box 299
Carthage, IL 62321-0299

Unless otherwise indicated, the King James version of the Bible was used in preparing the activities in this book.

DEDICATION

For Katy, Jack and Mary

With love,
Paulinus

For my grandfather, Frank

Aunt Helen

Bill Cooper

Aunt Marguerite

Love,
Carole

 SS880

INTRODUCTION

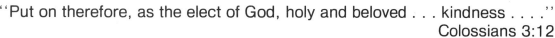

"Put on therefore, as the elect of God, holy and beloved . . . kindness . . . ."
Colossians 3:12

Jesus revealed the kingdom of God by reaching out in kindness to many people. Children, sinners, and the sick and lonely were all touched by His compassionate love. Jesus spilled the oil and wine of His kindness into the wounds of all those who were burdened. By His example He showed His followers how to be kind, and He also told stories to relate how kindness could be manifested in daily living.

We must bring kindness to others because God is their Father and they are good. We should let kindness show in our faces, our eyes and our smiles. People should leave us feeling better and happier.

The purpose of this book is to aid educators in teaching children about this compassionate virtue of kindness. Contained in this book are work sheets, games, songs, puzzles and a prayer service that will motivate children to learn about God's kindness, the kindness of others and their own kindness. These unique activities can be completed either individually or in a group. A scriptural passage about kindness is listed at the top of each idea, and more references are given in the back of the book for reflection or to embellish the activities.

SS880

TABLE OF CONTENTS

KIND WORDS

"And he said, Blessed be thou of the Lord, my daughter: for thou hast shown more kindness . . . ."

Ruth 3:10

Kind words tell others of God's kindness and love for each one of us. Decode the following messages. Then fold a paper in fourths. Write one decoded message in each space, and draw a picture for each message. (Use both sides of your paper.)

1. W M K   S   O U T B?

_____

2. S   T H A U   K H G.

_____

3. R H W U   M Y F   B T M K.

_____

4. S   M W   J H D D K.

_____

5. S   B D M K   C H D   K H G.

_____

6. S   B G N   N O U   N H K J   M I M K.

_____

7. S   J U N   N O U   N M P T U.

_____

8. W K   H I Y   S F U M.

_____

CODE:

A = V	K = Y	U = E
B = P	L = Z	V = J
C = F	M = A	W = M
D = R	N = T	X = Q
E = X	O = H	Y = N
F = D	P = B	Z = G
G = U	Q = K	
H = O	R = C	
I = W	S = I	
J = S	T = L	

THE IMPORTANCE OF KINDNESS

"By pureness, by knowledge, by longsuffering, by kindness . . . ."

II Corinthians 6:6

Interview three people. Ask each one to state ways in which kindness is important in daily living. Add these statements to the classroom bulletin board entitled "The Importance of Kindness."

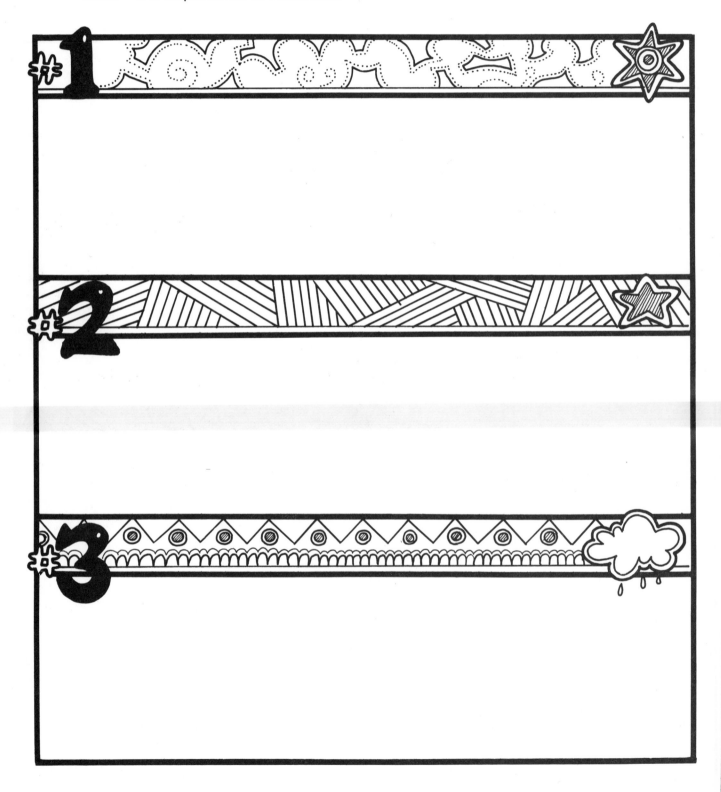

SS880

KINDNESS GAME

''And when Jesus saw her, he called her to him, and said unto her, Woman thou art loosed from thine infirmity.''

Luke 13:12

In the story of the crippled woman as told in Luke 13:10-13, we see Jesus' loving kindness for those He met. This game shows us something of what it means to be kind.

Two can play. The game sheet above may be mounted on a file folder or heavy tag and laminated or covered with clear Con-Tact. The cards are similarly mounted. Markers may be of heavy paper of two different colors, or the traditional *X's* and *O's* could be used.

The clue cards are placed face down on the table. After choosing a card, the player reads the clue and gives a word indicated by the letter on the card that tells about kindness. If the answer is correct, he places a marker on the gameboard. The player who first has five markers in a row—down, across or diagonally—wins. Answers which are correct but not identical with the answer sheet should be counted.

SS880

KINDNESS GAME
(cont'd.)

1. Giving help.   A
    Example: Assistance
	12. Unselfish. G	23. Divide and give a part to
		    another. S

2. Books containing the Word
    of God.   B
    Example: Bible
	13. Pleasant and courteous.
	    G
		24. Work people do for others.
		    S

3. Joy or gladness. C	14. Giving assistance. H	25. Sharing another's sorrow or trouble. S

4. Makes sorrow easier to
    bear.   C
	15. Gentle and friendly treat-
	    ment. K
		26. Kind, affectionate and lov-
		    ing. T

5. Thoughtful of others' feel-
    ings.   C
	16. Being gentle and good
	    rather than disagreeable.
	    K
		27. Kind, sympathetic. T

6. Generous giving to the
    helpless.   C
	17. Pays attention and tries to
	    hear. L
		28. Being loyal and honest. T

7. Benevolent and kind. C	18. Warm and tender feel-
	    ings. L
		29. Firm belief in the honesty
		    of another. T

8. Trust and rely on some-
    one for help.   D
	19. Kindness beyond what
	    justice demands. M
		30. Willingness to let another
		    do as he thinks best. T

9. Help increase hope and confidence. E	20. Willing to do a favor. O	31. Considerate of others. U

10. Polite and thoughtful be-
    havior.   C
	21. Feeling for the distress of
	    another. P
		32. Sympathetic to another's
		    feelings. U

11. Willingness to share. G	22. Act of speaking to God. P	33. Friendly and affectionate to others. W

SS880

KINDNESS IS WORTH A FORTUNE

A popular custom associated with the Chinese is the serving of fortune cookies. These treats contain strips of paper with words of wisdom, often from the philosopher Confucius. Confucius' teachings about respect for others, responsibility, and compassion of the heart are a strong influence in Chinese society. The Bible also encourages us to act with kindness and compassion to others. Find some verses from the Bible that will help you remember to treat others kindly. Write them on the fortune cookies below. Then color and cut out the cookies, and share them with your friends. Choose one or two sayings from cookies you receive and memorize them.

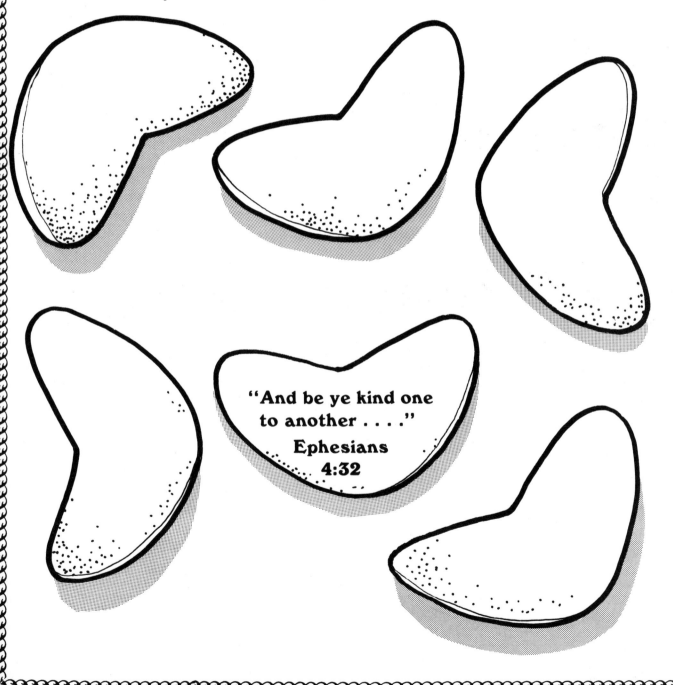

"And be ye kind one to another . . . ."
Ephesians 4:32

 SS880

KINDNESS IN THE BIBLE
GOD'S KINDNESS IN CREATING

"That in the ages to come he might show the exceeding riches of his grace in his kindness toward us through Christ Jesus."   Ephesians 2:7

Think of all the things that our kind Father has created for us. Go outside and take pictures of your favorite ones.

Take a nature walk and silently thank God for all His kindness to us.

Write words and draw pictures of your favorite things in nature.

_____

_____

_____

_____

_____

_____

_____

_____

SUPPOSE

"And when the Lord saw her, he had compassion on her . . . ."   Luke 7:13

Suppose your husband was dead. You had only one child. Then just as your child was old enough to help support both of you, he suddenly became sick and died. While the funeral procession was on its way to the cemetery, a large crowd passed by. One man stepped out of the crowd and put His hand on your shoulder. Then He touched your son, and your son sat up and began to talk. How did you feel? Describe your feelings in two sentences.

1._____

2._____

Read the story of the Widow of Nain in Luke 7:11-17. Write a story about what happened **after** your son was restored. Talk about your feelings. Was your life different from the way it was before? How did your friends treat you? Your son? Did you ever see Jesus again? Write in the space below.

_____

_____

_____

_____

_____

_____

_____

_____

_____

_____

Shining Star Publications, Copyright © 1987, A division of Good Apple, Inc.   SS880

JESUS TALKS ABOUT KINDNESS

"...go, and do thou likewise."   Luke 10:37

Once Jesus was talking about charity to some people. One of His listeners tried to make excuses for not being kind. Jesus told the story of a Samaritan who stopped on the road to help someone who was hurt. As you travel through this maze, think about how you can be kind to someone— your classmate, your brother, even someone you do not know.

START

Robbers strip and beat traveler, leaving him half dead.

Others pass by but do nothing to help.

Samaritan stops and puts medicine and bandages on wounds.

Samaritan puts traveler on his own donkey.

Samaritan takes traveler to inn and pays for his care.

END

Read the story Jesus told in Luke 10:30-37. Write one sentence telling how you can help someone.

_____

_____

SS880

JESUS HELPS US BE KIND

''And he said unto them . . . with what measure ye mete, it shall be measured
to you . . . .''

Mark 4:24

Jesus told the people many stories to show how they could become closer
friends with God by helping those they met. But more than this, He showed
how to be kind by the way He treated those He met. Many of these stories are
listed below. Read the stories in your Bible. Then rearrange the letters to find
their titles. Use the circled letters to answer the question at the bottom.

1. E E H L O P S S T   Matthew 18:11-14

Ⓞ _ _ _   _ _ _ _ _

2. A C H I M N R   Luke 16:19-31

_ _ _ Ⓞ _ _ _

3. E E F G I N O R S S V   Luke 17:3,4

_ _ Ⓞ _ _ _ _ Ⓞ _ _ _

4. E E E L N P R S T   Luke 17:11-19

Ⓞ _ _   _ _ Ⓞ _ _ _

5. M R R A A E G I A E F S T   Matthew 22:1-4

_ _ _ _ _ _ Ⓞ _   _ _ _ _ _

6. A E E I O R T T N W W   John 2:1-11

_ _ _ _ _ Ⓞ _ _   _ _ _ _

7. O O D G D E E H H P R S   John 10:1-21

_ _ _ _   _ _ _ _ Ⓞ _ _ _

8. A C D E M N O R U W   Luke 13:10-13

Ⓞ _ _ _ _   Ⓞ _ _ _ _

9. A L M P   Mark 4:21-24   (New International Version)

_ _ _ Ⓞ

10. B D E I L M N N   Matthew 20:29-34

Ⓞ _ _ _ _   _ _ _

11. D I N O O S S W W   Luke 7:11-17

_ _ _ _ _ _ ,_ Ⓞ _ _

12. A D G I L N O O P S R   Luke 15:11-32

_ _ _ Ⓞ _ _ _   _ _ _

QUESTION: What does Jesus want us to do? _ _ _ _   _ _ _   _ _ _ _ _ _ _ _
                                         2 4 1 9   8 8 3   3 4 12 5 7 10 11 6

Shining Star Publications, Copyright © 1987, A division of Good Apple, Inc.   SS880

VIEWING JESUS' KINDNESS

"... but with everlasting kindness will I have mercy on thee, saith the Lord thy Redeemer."

Isaiah 54:8

Draw pictures of some of your favorite miracles and record them on the film below. Write the event and the reference beside each frame. Examples of appropriate scriptural passages are on pages 30 and 31.

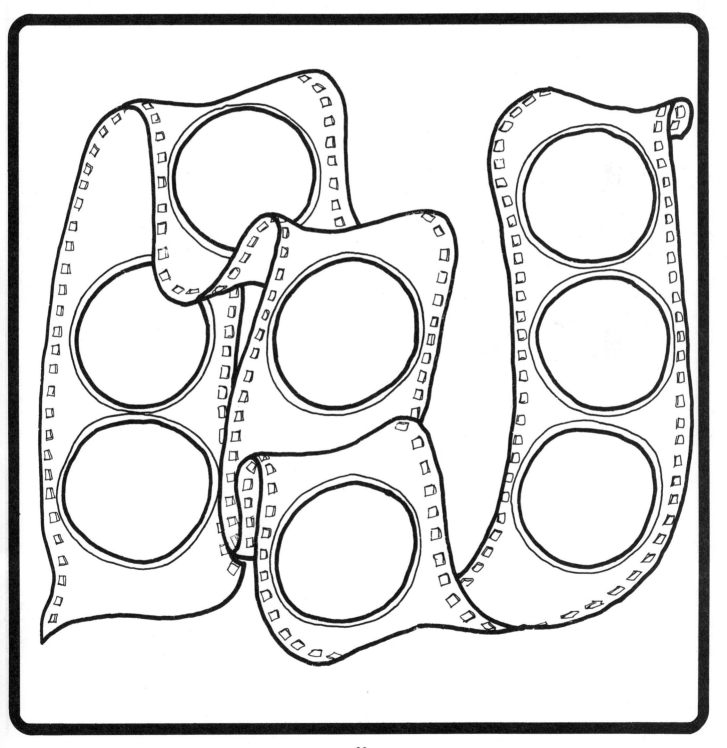

SS880

KIND PEOPLE

''And went to him, and bound up his wounds . . . .''   Luke 10:34

Many times in our lives we encounter someone in extreme need who deserves our help even if it is inconvenient or difficult for us to give it. Below are many Bible people who faced the same problem. See if you can unscramble their names. At the right are clues that may help you. Then look up the Bible references and read the stories again.

On another sheet of paper, write the story of one of these people of great kindness.

1. A L U P
_ _ _ _
He wrote letters to his friends telling them how wonderful they were. (I Thessalonians 1:4-7)

2. A A A I M N S T R
_ _ _ _ _ _ _ _ _
He took a wounded man to the inn and paid for his expenses. (Luke 10:30-36)

3. A D D I V
_ _ _ _ _
He refused to harm the man who was trying to kill him. (I Samuel 24:2-8)

4. A A A B H M R
_ _ _ _ _ _ _
He invited three strangers to stay at his house and have dinner with him and his wife. (Genesis 18:1-8)

5. A A I L Q U
_ _ _ _ _ _
He shared his home with a fellow tentmaker. (Acts 18:1-3)

6. A B O Z
_ _ _ _
He gave a young woman six measures of barley to take to her mother-in-law. (Ruth 3:16,17)

7. A A B H R
_ _ _ _ _
She helped two Israelite soldiers by hiding them under the flax on her roof. (Joshua 2:3-22)

8. A M R Y
_ _ _ _
She felt sorry when the bride and groom ran out of wine for their wedding celebration. (John 2:1-3)

9. A E H I L J
_ _ _ _ _ _
The son of a widow was brought back to life when he prayed for him. (I Kings 17:17-24)

10. A I M N O
_ _ _ _ _
She helped her daughter-in-law find a new husband. (Ruth 3:1-6)

11. A D J H U
_ _ _ _ _
He offered to go to prison in Egypt so his brother might go back to his father. (Genesis 44:8-33)

12. A C E L O P S
_ _ _ _ _ _ _
He invited a stranger he met on the way to Emmaus to stay and have dinner with him. (Luke 24:28-30)

13. A C I L L P S R I
_ _ _ _ _ _ _ _ _
She and her husband taught Apollos about Christianity. (Acts 18:24-26)

14. E H I N O O P R S U S
_ _ _ _ _ _ _ _ _ _
He comforted Paul in prison but died before he could return to his own city. (II Timothy 1:16-18)

15. D E H U A I O P P R T S
_ _ _ _ _ _ _ _ _ _ _
He risked his life to save Paul. (Philippians 2:25-30)

16. E E H R S T
_ _ _ _ _ _
This queen risked her life to save her people, the Jews, from a plot to kill them. (Esther 4:15,16)

UNTO OTHERS

''. . . Inasmuch as ye have done it unto one of the least of these my brethren, ye have done it unto me.''

Matthew 25:40

In the story told in I Kings 17:10-26, the widow of Zarephath was willing to give the last bit of meal she had in the house to the weary traveler who asked for food. Below are the names of many others who showed kindness to others while forgetting their own comfort and need. The names help us think about kindness. See how many you can find.

The letters may follow in any direction; up, down, backward, forward or even twist. The same letter may be used in different words. More than one person may compete. The one finding the most names wins.

PEOPLE WHO WERE KIND:

Aquila	Abraham	Epaphroditus	Boaz	Cleophas
David	Elijah	Me	Jesus	Jonathan
Judas	Mary	Rahab	Naomi	Nicodemus
Paul	Prisca	Susanna	Ruth	Salome
Samaritan	Simon	Us		

SS880

KINDNESS KWIZ

"And when he saw them, he said unto them, Go show yourselves to the priests ...."

Luke 17:14

Jesus revealed the Kingdom of God by his preaching and by the many kindnesses He showed to those in need. One of these kind acts was the curing of the ten lepers on His way to Jerusalem.

Luke 17:11-19

We too must show others the way to heaven by the way we treat them. There are many examples of kindness in the Bible for us to imitate. See if you can match the names of persons with the kind acts they performed.

1. Cleopas ____

2. Samaritan ____

3. Mary ____

4. Rahab ____

5. Jonathan ____

6. Prisca (Priscilla) ____

7. Ruth ____

8. Widow of Zaraphath ____

9. Joanna and friends ____

10. David ____

11. Aquila ____

12. Joseph ____

13. Judah ____

14. Abraham ____

15. Jesus ____

a. She went to help her mother-in-law on her way back to Bethlehem.

b. He offered to go to prison in Egypt so his brother might go home to his father.

c. He took a wounded man to the inn and paid for his expenses.

d. He hugged the children and played with them.

e. He refused to harm the man who was trying to kill him.

f. He invited the stranger he met on the way to Emmaus to come in and have dinner with him.

g. She helped two Israelite soldiers by hiding them under the flax on her roof.

h. He invited three strangers to stay at his house and have dinner with him and his wife.

i. He risked his life to warn his best friend of danger.

j. She used her last bit of cornmeal to make bread for a stranger.

k. They provided services and food for Jesus and the Twelve.

l. She and her husband taught Apollos about Christianity.

m. She felt sorry when the bride and groom ran out of wine for their wedding celebration.

n. He shared his home with a fellow tentmaker.

o. He gave a feast for his brothers to show them he forgave them.

Shining Star Publications, Copyright © 1987, A division of Good Apple, Inc.

SS880

REACH OUT IN KINDNESS

"And now the Lord show kindness and truth unto you: and I also will requite you this kindness, because ye have done this thing."   II Samuel 2:6

Jesus reached out in kindness to many people. Write some examples on the left hand.

List ways that you can reach out to others in kindness and write them on the right hand.

27

SS880

RUTH AND NAOMI

"And Naomi said unto her daughter-in-law, Blessed be he of the Lord, who hath not left off his kindness to the living and to the dead. And Naomi said unto her, The man is near of kin unto us, one of our next kinsmen."   Ruth 2:20

The story of Ruth's devotion to her mother-in-law and Naomi's love for Ruth provides warmth and beauty amid the often violent war stories of the Old Testament. The kindness of these two women for each other, and of Boaz for each of them, shows a different side of life in Judea. It is a heartwarming example for each of us.

Pretend that you are either Ruth or Naomi and write to Orpah, describing some part of what happened after you left her in Moab.

These are some of the questions you may need to think about before you start writing.

1. Who was Naomi's husband? Why did they move to Moab?
2. Who was Ruth's first husband? Why did Ruth move from Moab to Judea?
3. Who was Orpah? What was her husband's name? Why did Orpah not go to Judea with Ruth and Naomi?

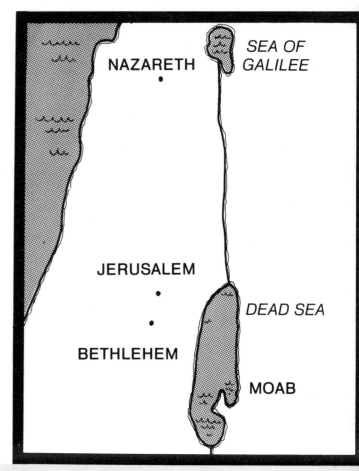

4. What town did Ruth and Naomi live in when they returned to Judea?
5. How did Ruth and Naomi get their food when they returned?
6. Who was Ruth's second husband? How did she meet him?
7. Who was Obed? What was his relationship to David? to Jesus?
8. What did Naomi think of Obed? How did she treat him?

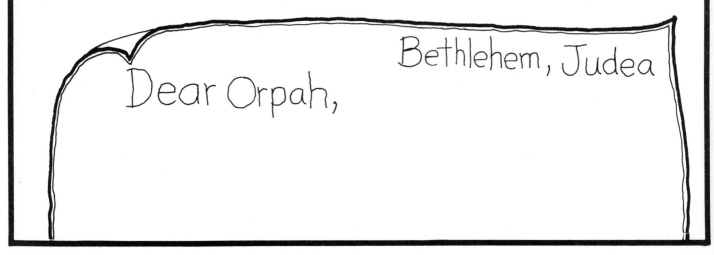

Bethlehem, Judea

Dear Orpah,

LAST WILL AND TESTAMENT

"... it shall be a kindness ...."

Psalm 141:5

What treasured possessions would biblical characters will to each other? Use your imagination and write your ideas below. Some examples are given to help you get started.

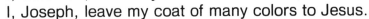

I, Solomon, leave my wisdom to Peter.
I, Joseph, leave my coat of many colors to Jesus.

Shining Star Publications, Copyright © 1987, A division of Good Apple, Inc.

SS880

MIRACLE BANNER

"... but thou art a God ... of great kindness ...." Nehemiah 9:17

Why do you think Jesus performed miracles? Which of His many miracles do you think is the most wonderful? Why?

One way to celebrate the miracles of Jesus is to make a Miracle Banner. It is easy to do. All you will need is a long piece of ribbon, construction paper, crayons or marking pens, and glue. Illustrate miracles performed by Jesus on construction paper. Attach each miracle to the ribbon. When you are finished, label your banner and hang it where everyone can enjoy it. Here are some scriptural passages that will help you.

Matthew 17:14-21	Luke 17:11-19
Matthew 8:5-15	Luke 8:26-39
Matthew 14:13-33	John 11:1-44
Matthew 9:18-31	John 4:46-54
Mark 7:31-37	John 5:1-9

TELL IT TO SOLOMON

Decorate the front of a shoe box to look like King Solomon. Put a slit in the top. Students can write down their problems, joys, dreams, feelings, etc., and share these with Solomon. A supply of index cards should be kept nearby at all times. After school the teacher can read the cards and write responses on those that are signed. She can then slip them into the students' desks.

SS880

NEWSPAPER STORY

"Jesus saith unto them, Fill the waterpots with water . . . ."   John 2:7

Search the Scriptures for an account of a miracle performed by Jesus. Some references and topics are given to help you get started. Write a newspaper article describing this miracle as if you were an eyewitness.

Jesus heals a leper. Matthew 8:1-4

Jesus heals a servant. Matthew 8:5-13

Jesus heals Peter's mother-in-law. Matthew 8:14-15

Jesus heals a palsied man. Matthew 9:1-8

Jesus raises Jairus' daughter from the dead. Matthew 9:18-26

Jesus gives two blind men their sight. Matthew 9:27-31

Jesus casts out a demon. Matthew 9:32-33

the *Christian* news

JESUS _____

_____

_____

_____

_____

_____

_____

_____

_____

_____

_____

_____

WORKS OF KINDNESS

"... Inasmuch as ye have done it unto one of the least of these my brethren, ye have done it unto me."

Matthew 25:40

Jesus tells us in the story of the King of Heaven (Matthew 25:31-40) that whatever we do for others we do for Him. Sometimes we are surprised at the value of such small acts. But how much more important are those things which we do for the souls of others.

In the space below are examples of such acts. In each box write your own examples of spiritual acts of kindness.

ADVISE THE SINNER Try to keep your friend from stealing by reminding him how wrong it is.	**TEACH THE UNEDUCATED** Help your little sister learn her prayers.
GUIDE THE DOUBTFUL Answer questions about why you do not say bad words or look at bad pictures.	**COMFORT THE SORROWFUL** Put your arms around someone when others make fun of him.
BEAR WRONGS PATIENTLY Accept your brother's thoughtlessness when he loses or breaks your toys.	**FORGIVE ALL INJURIES** Try to do something nice for someone when he apologizes.

SS880

REACH OUT WITH KINDNESS

ROOTED IN KINDNESS

"She openeth her mouth with wisdom; and in her tongue is the law of kindness."

Proverbs 31:26

On the family tree below, write down the names of your family members and about times when you helped them or when they helped you.

Name

Name

Name

Name

Name

Name

Me

SS880

I AM KIND

"And to godliness brotherly kindness; and to brotherly kindness charity."

II Peter 1:7

Draw yourself in the pictures below. Show how you can help turn these scenes into happy ones.

CAN I HELP?

"Hereby perceive we the love of God, because he laid down his life for us . . . ."
I John 3:16

We need to be kind to many people. We help them because God is their Father and because they are good. To be kind and loving, we do what we can for them, helping them when they need us.

In his letter James tells us about helping. Read what he has to say in James 2:14-17. Or read what John tells us in I John 3:16,17. Then fill in the chart below to tell how you would show your friendship for God and kindness to those near you.

NEED	WHAT I WOULD DO	HOW I WOULD DO IT
It snowed. Grandmother needs her walk cleared.		
Baby is crying.		
Father can't find his hammer.		
Mother must go shopping. The dishes are not finished.		
Your playmate is sick and lonely.		

SS880

BE KIND TO ANIMALS CLUB

''O Lord, how manifold are thy works ! . . .''   Psalm 104:24

As we study the habits and powers of living creatures, we realize what a great, mysterious thing life is. Through the beauty of His creatures we know the love and kindness of God who created them and cares for them. We also learn how we must treat them.

Suppose you are organizing or are a member of a BE KIND TO ANIMALS CLUB. Write a speech you could give your club about animal treatment. Your speech could be about any wild animals such as birds, squirrels, rabbits, caterpillars, or bugs. Or it might be about domestic animals such as cows, horses, sheep, or other farm animals. Perhaps you might even wish to talk about pets who have no homes.

Choose one animal and tell what you might do to show kindness for it in imitation of God's care. Tell where you would find the animal and how you would treat it. What are its needs? Why would you do what you choose to do for it?

Read Genesis 1:20-25 and Psalm 104 as you prepare your speech. You may wish to quote one of these Scripture passages in your speech.

Shining Star Publications, Copyright © 1987, A division of Good Apple, Inc.   SS880

KINDNESS TO PETS

''. . . according to the kindness that I have done unto thee, thou shalt do unto me . . . .''
                                                                    Genesis 21:23

Everywhere we look we see that God's creation is wonderfully planned. The millions of stars, the mountains clothed in trees, the ocean in its depths are His creations. More wonderful yet are the living things that He has made.

In being kind to our pets, we imitate God in His love for us and in His kindness and care for all of His creatures. In the space below tell how you show kindness to your pet in imitation of God's great love. If you have no pet, pretend you have one, and write a story about how you would treat it.

These are things you may wish to think about before you write:

Is your pet fed regularly? Who feeds it? Does it get plenty of exercise? Does anyone play with it? How? Who trained it to be a good pet? How? What rules do you follow to keep it from getting hurt? Do you ever tease it? Do you ever do anything which might bring it harm? How does your pet react to you?

SS880

SAND PAINTING

"... thou hast shown kindness ...."   Genesis 24:14

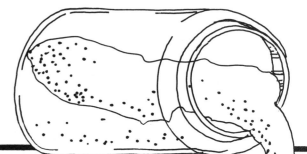

Make a sand picture to give to someone or for your room, showing how you can grow in kindness toward others.

DIRECTIONS:

Obtain fine, preferably white, clean sand. Dye the sand using regular all-purpose dye (Rit), food coloring (preferably paste rather than liquid), or tempera paints. Experiment with the dyes and the amount of water until you get the colors you want. Remember that when the sand is wet it will be much darker than when it dries. Dry the sand by spreading it out on waxed paper. Store in jars, so you can see the colors.

TO PAINT:

Draw the outline of the picture you want to paint. Decide on colors. Mix Elmer's glue with an equal amount of water. Brush glue on design, covering only the area for *one* color at a time. Then sprinkle that color of sand on the design. Let stand a few minutes to dry; shake off excess sand onto a piece of paper so that it may be returned to the jar for use again. Put lighter colors on first. Continue brushing glue and sprinkling sand until all colors are on.

These are some ideas you can use for your pictures:

1. Share some treasure.
2. Give a soft answer.
3. Gladden someone's heart.
4. Write a letter.
5. Find time for a friend.
6. Mend a quarrel.
7. Help your neighbor.
8. Take care of baby for Mother.
9. Encourage your classmate.
10. Pray for someone in need.
11. Use your own idea.

38

SS880

STARDUST

"... I will show kindness ...."

I Chronicles 19:2

Sometimes we forget that we should be kind to the groups of people of whom we are a part. We are kind when we do a service for them. Or we are kind when we act in such a way that we reflect credit upon them. In the star are five groups to which we belong. Write one kind act for each group. Then decorate your star and hang it in your room. Or you may wish to use it for a bulletin board entitled "Stardust."

SOMETHING KIND FOR THE WORLD

SOMETHING KIND FOR MY SCHOOL

SOMETHING KIND FOR MY FAMILY

SOMETHING KIND FOR MYSELF

SOMETHING KIND FOR MY CHURCH

SOMETHING KIND FOR MY NEIGHBORHOOD

39

SS880

KIND DEEDS

"And thou shalt not only while yet I live show me the kindness of the Lord . . . ."

I Samuel 20:14

We have many opportunities to show kindness at home and to our playmates and neighbors. Think about the following situations and discuss them with your friends and classmates. Then draw cartoon pictures to illustrate them.

1. Laurie cleaned her room without being told.
2. Ruth dried the dishes cheerfully.
3. Jack stopped playing with his computer to help Bill with a math problem.
4. Joan took out the garbage without being asked.
5. Alice shared her candy with Sandy.
6. Bobby raked the leaves and bagged them for his father.
7. The children from First Street cleaned the vacant lot.
8. Tom let Jimmy ride his bike.
9. The children collected canned goods for the family whose father had died.
10. Gloria hurried home to do the chores for her mother.
11. Dick helped his mother with the baby.
12. Carl cleaned the basement without being paid.
13. Rachel was careful not to exclude anyone from her group.
14. Jerry had a good sense of humor and tried to make others feel happy.
15. I will do a kind deed of my own choosing.
16. I will follow my classmate's suggestion.

SS880

BAKE A CLASS COOKIE

"... do show kindness this day ...."   II Samuel 3:8

Prepare a giant chocolate-chip cookie. Follow the recipe found on a chocolate-chip package.

1. Turn the oven to 325 degrees. Place a rack in the center of the oven.
2. Cover a 12-inch pizza pan with foil, crimping the edges. Grease the foil lightly and trace a 10-inch circle in the shortening. Set the pan on a cookie sheet.
3. Measure 3 cups of dough into the center of the pan. Use your fingers to smooth the dough over the 10-inch circle.
4. Bake about 25 minutes; then cover with a sheet of heavy foil. Bake about 20 minutes more, checking often after 10 minutes.
5. When the cookie puffs and falls back and feels firm in the center, it is done.
6. Remove the cookie carefully and cool on a wire rack. Place it on a cool cookie sheet and decorate if desired.
7. Enjoy!

Shining Star Publications, Copyright © 1987, A division of Good Apple, Inc.   SS880

TYPES OF GIVING

"Put on therefore, as the elect of God, holy and beloved . . . mercies, kindness, humbleness of mind, meekness, longsuffering." Colossians 3:12

Below are some examples of different types of giving. Give your own example of each type.

CONDITIONAL GIVING
I will pick up a loaf of bread for you, if I am going to the store.

I will_____

if I _____

FREE GIVING
I will go for a bicycle ride with you because I like you.

I will_____

because _____

RELUCTANT GIVING
I will help you do your homework, but I really do not have the time.

I will_____

but I _____

BARTERED GIVING
I will do the dishes for you, if you will help me take out the garbage.

I will_____

if you _____

Which type of giving do you do the most?

Which type of giving is typical of Jesus? He encourages us to follow His example.

_____

_____

_____

_____

_____

_____

Shining Star Publications, Copyright © 1987, A division of Good Apple, Inc.   SS880

BRIDGING KINDNESS

"And David said unto him, Fear not: for I will surely show thee kindness . . . ."

II Samuel 9:7

Instead of building a wall between yourself and a friend, build a bridge of kindness to unite you. Write words on the bridge that unite friends in kindness.

SS880

LIVING BY THE GOLDEN RULE

Words by Helen Kitchell Evans
Music by Frances Mann Benson

I am so hap-py in church and school. I try to live by the Gold-en Rule

I try to treat every-one I see as I would have them treat me.

The Golden Rule · KINDNESS

SS880

PRAYER CELEBRATION OF KINDNESS

"Put on therefore, as the elect of God, holy and beloved . . . kindness . . . ."

Colossians 3:12

HYMN:	"Living by the Golden Rule" p.44
OPENING PRAYER:	Jesus, you were always kind to people, helping and healing them each day. Teach us how to be kind, not only to our friends and families, but to all those we meet. Amen.
FIRST READING:	Colossians 3:12-15 (An adaptation) Because you are loved and chosen by God, clothe yourselves with mercy, kindness, meekness and patience. Put up with one another; forgive as the Lord has forgiven you. Over all these virtues put on love, which binds the rest together and makes them perfect.
HEART-FELT KINDNESS:	Distribute small hearts made from felt and pin one on each child.
SECOND READING:	Matthew 25:34-40 (An adaptation) Come, children. You have my Father's blessing. Inherit the kingdom which has been prepared for you. For I was hungry and you gave me food; I was thirsty and you gave me drink. I was a stranger and you welcomed me, naked and you clothed me. I was ill and you comforted me, in prison and you came to visit me. As often as you did it for one of my least brothers, you did it for me.
SILENT REFLECTION:	Let us thank God for all those who have shown us kindness.
BLESSING:	Let us go forth with acts of kindness and serve others!

KINDNESS CONTRACT

I promise to be kind to _____

by _____

_____
Signature

SS880

MEDAL OF KINDNESS

"... that ye have shown this kindness ...."

II Samuel 2:5

PRESENTED TO: _____

FOR: _____

BY: _____

SS880

ANSWER KEY

CROSSWORD PUZZLE p. 10

ACROSS
1. Considerate
7. Woe
8. Good
10. Please
14. U.K.
17. Forgiving
20. Need
21. Meet
22. Glad
24. Poor
25. Give
26. Death
27. Peace
28. Man
30. Love
31. Mercy
34. Fact
36. Red
37. Who
38. Sympathy

DOWN
2. Owl
3. Noel
4. Sea
5. Take
6. Courage
9. Donor
11. Self
12. Hug
13. Concern
15. Kindness
16. Help
18. I'm
19. Neighbor
22. Gracious
23. Feed
27. Patch
29. Dye
32. Eat
33. Cry
35. Awe

KIND WORDS p. 13

1. May I help? 2. I love you.
3. Come and play. 4. I am sorry.
5. I pray for you. 6. I put the toys away. 7. I set the table. 8. My own idea.

KINDNESS p. 16

1. Assistance—Giving help
2. Bible—Books containing the word of God
3. Cheer—Joy or gladness
4. Comfort—Makes sorrow easier to bear
5. Considerate—Thoughtful of others' feelings
6. Charity—Generous giving to the helpless
7. Charitable—Benevolent and kind
8. Depend—Trust and rely on someone for help
9. Encourage—Help increase hope and confidence
10. Courtesy—Polite and thoughtful behavior
11. Generosity—Willingness to share
12. Generous—Unselfish
13. Gracious—Pleasant and courteous
14. Helpful—Giving assistance
15. Kindness—Gentle and friendly treatment
16. Kind—Being gentle and good rather than disagreeable
17. Listens—Pays attention and tries to hear
18. Love—Warm and tender feelings
19. Mercy—Kindness beyond that which justice demands
20. Obliging—Willing to do a favor
21. Pity—Feeling for the distress of another
22. Prayer—Act of speaking to God
23. Share—Divide and give a part to another
24. Service—Work people do for others
25. Sympathy—Sharing another's sorrow or trouble
26. Tender—Kind, affectionate and loving
27. Tender-hearted—Kind, sympathetic
28. Trustworthy—Being loyal and honest
29. Trust—Firm belief in the honesty of another
30. Tolerance—Willingness to let another do as he thinks best
31. Unselfish—Considerate of others
32. Understanding—Sympathetic to another's feelings
33. Warm-hearted—Friendly and affectionate to others

JESUS HELPS US BE KIND p. 22

1. Lost Sheep 2. Rich Man 3. Forgiveness 4. Ten Lepers
5. Marriage Feast 6. Water to Wine 7. Good Shepherd
8. Cured Woman 9. Lamp 10. Blind Men 11. Widow's Son
12. Prodigal Son

ANSWER TO QUESTION: Help our neighbor.

KIND PEOPLE p. 24

1. Paul 2. Samaritan 3. David 4. Abraham 5. Aquila 6. Boaz
7. Rahab 8. Mary 9. Elijah 10. Naomi 11. Judah 12. Cleopas
13. Priscilla 14. Onesiphorus 15. Epaphroditus 16. Esther

KINDNESS KWIZ p. 26

1-f (Luke 24:18-29) 2-c (Luke 10:30-37) 3-m (John 2:1-2) 4-g (Joshua 2:3-7) 5-i (I Samuel 19:1-7) 6-1 (Acts 18:24-26) 7-a (Ruth 1:14-18) 8-j (I Kings 17:10-16) 9-k (Luke 8:2,3) 10-e (I Samuel 24:2-18) 11-n (Acts 18:1-3) 12-o (Genesis 43:30-34) 13-b (Genesis 44:18-33) 14-h (Genesis 18:1-8) 15-d (Mark 10:13-16)

SCRIPTURAL PASSAGES ON KINDNESS

Genesis 20:13; 21:23; 24:12; 40:14
Joshua 2:12
Judges 8:35
Ruth 2:20; 3:10
I Samuel 15:6; 20:14; 20:15
II Samuel 2:5; 2:6; 3:8; 9:1; 9:3, 9:7; 10:2; 16:17
I Kings 2:7; 3:6
I Chronicles 19:2
II Chronicles 24:22
Nehemiah 9:17
Esther 2:9
Psalms 31:21; 141:5
Proverbs 19:22; 31:26
Isaiah 54:8
Jeremiah 2:2
Joel 2:13
Jonah 4:2
Acts 28:2
II Corinthians 6:6
Ephesians 2:7
Colossians 3:12
II Peter 1:7

Shining Star Publications, Copyright © 1987, A division of Good Apple, Inc.

SS880